SUGAR

Rhoda Nottridge

Illustrations by John Yates

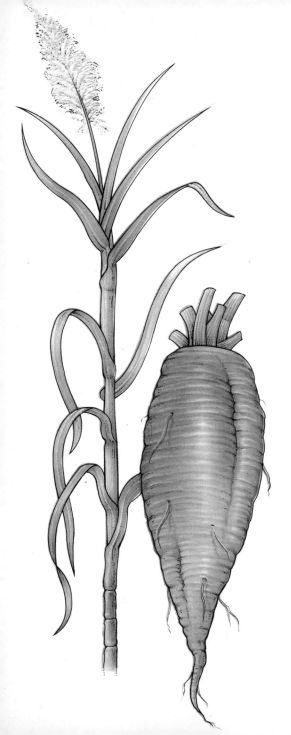

Food

Apples	**Herbs and spices**
Beans and pulses	**Meat**
Bread	**Milk**
Butter	**Potatoes**
Cakes and biscuits	**Rice**
Cheese	**Sugar**
Citrus fruit	**Tea**
Eggs	**Vegetables**
Fish	

All words that appear in **bold** are explained in the glossary on page 30.

Editor: Fiona Corbridge

First published in 1989 by Wayland (Publishers) Limited
61 Western Road, Hove, East Sussex BN3 1JD, England.

© Copyright 1989 Wayland (Publishers) Limited

British Library Cataloguing in Publication Data
Nottridge, Rhoda
  Sugar. (Food).
  1. Sugar
  I. Title   II. Series

ISBN 1–85210–265–9

Typeset by Kalligraphics Ltd., Horley, Surrey
Printed in Italy by G.Canale C.S.p.A., Turin
Bound by Casterman S.A., Belgium

Contents

What is sugar?

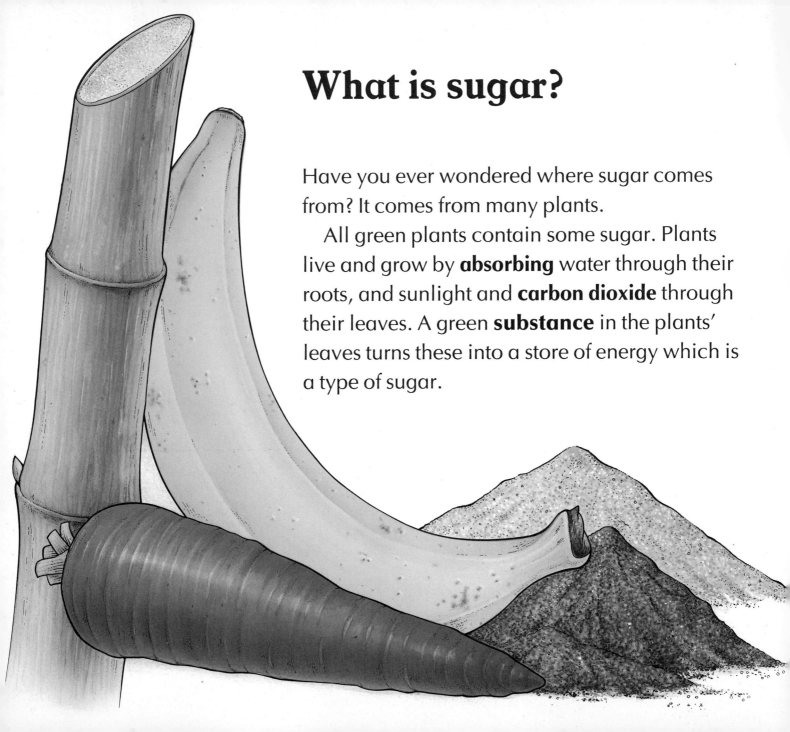

Have you ever wondered where sugar comes from? It comes from many plants.

All green plants contain some sugar. Plants live and grow by **absorbing** water through their roots, and sunlight and **carbon dioxide** through their leaves. A green **substance** in the plants' leaves turns these into a store of energy which is a type of sugar.

We can taste the sugar in plants most easily when we eat sweet fruits. Although vegetables may not taste very sweet, when we eat them we eat a plant's store of sugar.

Some types of corn, and the sap from maple trees, produce sugar in a syrup form.

Most of the sugar we buy in the shops comes from two plants: the sugar cane and sugar beet. These plants have to go through a long factory process before they are turned into the sugar we buy in the shops.

Sugar around the world

Today, there is a huge demand for sugar in the world. The amount of sugar that each country uses varies greatly. For instance, the British use so much sugar that on average, each person consumes about 34 kg of sugar every year. In some African countries, the amount is less than 5 kg for each person a year. Industrialized countries use the most sugar.

This man is selling chunks of raw sugar cane in Lahore, Pakistan. These are a popular snack.

Left *Cutting down a towering crop of sugar cane. Cane grows to a height of about 5m.*

Below *Cane cutters on a sugar cane plantation in Cuba.*

Cuba, Brazil and India produce most of the cane sugar in the world. The USSR and the **European Economic Community** (EEC) grow the most sugar beet.

The sugar industry provides millions of jobs for people who work on farms, in sugar factories, and who transport sugar around the world. Some sugar companies have built schools and hospitals for their employees, and try to help the communities where the sugar is grown.

Sugar in the past

Above *Cutting sugar cane in the West Indies in the eighteenth century.*

People have used honey as a sweetener since the earliest times. Sugar from the sugar cane plant was first used at least 2,000 years ago, in the Far East. Gradually, people began to grow sugar cane in other countries too. It spread to India, North Africa and parts of the Mediterranean.

In the Middle Ages, the **crusaders** brought back sugar to Europe for the first time. Europe soon started to trade in sugar with the East. But

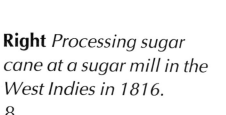

Right *Processing sugar cane at a sugar mill in the West Indies in 1816.*

8

Workers at a sugar refinery in Bristol in the nineteenth century.

sugar was a very expensive luxury, which only the very rich could afford to buy. It actually cost about 70 times more than it does today.

In 1493, the explorer Christopher Columbus took sugar cane plants from Spain and planted them in the West Indies. The sugar cane grew well in the Caribbean sun and rich soil, and so Europeans set up special farms to grow it, called plantations. The Europeans shipped over slaves from Africa and forced them to work on the plantations. The landowners soon grew rich by selling the sugar, called 'white gold', to Europe.

In the nineteenth century, Britain went to war against France. The British Navy blocked off many European ports, which cut off the supply of cane sugar coming across the sea from the Caribbean plantations.

Sugar beet had been grown in Europe for a long time, but only as a vegetable. When their

Making sugar from sugar beet at a French factory in the nineteenth century.

Sugar cane is traditionally harvested by hand, using machetes.

supplies of sugar cane were cut off by the British, the French discovered they could use beet to make sugar which tasted just as good as the sugar from cane. Slowly, other European countries started to grow beet as well. Unlike sugar cane, which needs lots of sun, sugar beet can grow in a cooler climate.

Today, sugar cane and beet are grown in many countries. The world now produces about 97 million tonnes of sugar every year!

Growing sugar cane

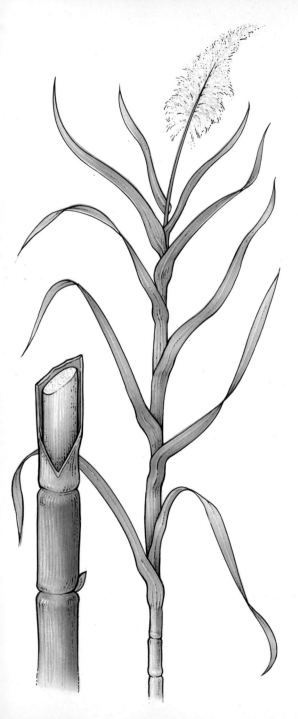

Sugar cane is a kind of very tall grass, which grows to a height of about 5m. It needs a **tropical** climate to grow, with plenty of strong sunlight and rainfall.

The sugar is stored in the long stalk of the plant, called the cane. Cane can be harvested at any time of the year, when the ground is dry and the farmer thinks the plant is big enough.

Sugar cane used to be cut down by hand, using a sharp knife, which was very hard, slow work. Today, it is nearly all cut down by machines.

When the cane is harvested, the roots of the plant are left in the ground. The following year, a new cane sprouts from the roots and grows.

Farmers may also grow new plants from cane cuttings, called setts.

Sugar cane is now grown in over 60 countries, from Australia to South America. Sugar cane actually provides 60 per cent of the world's supply of sugar.

Unloading sugar cane for sale at a market in Brazil.

Growing sugar beet

Harvesting sugar beet with a special harvesting machine.

Sugar beet grows well in a **temperate** climate, such as in European countries, the USA, Canada, the USSR, China and Japan.

Sugar beet is called a root vegetable, like parsnips or carrots, because the part we eat is the root that grows underground.

Sugar beet grows in a two-year cycle. In the first year, the root builds up a store of sugar as food, and swells to a weight of about 1kg. If the plant is left to grow, in the second year it will use its store of sugar to flower and produce seeds.

So the farmer harvests the plant at the end of the first year, when the root contains the most sugar. The harvesting machine cuts the leafy tops off the beet, and these are used for animal feed. The machine then lifts the root out of the ground and cleans off the earth.

Farmers grow new sugar beet plants from seeds. A machine is used to plant seeds in the soil in evenly spaced rows. While the crop is growing, the beet fields need to be weeded regularly. Farmers use machines to do this, or spray weedkiller to stop weeds growing.

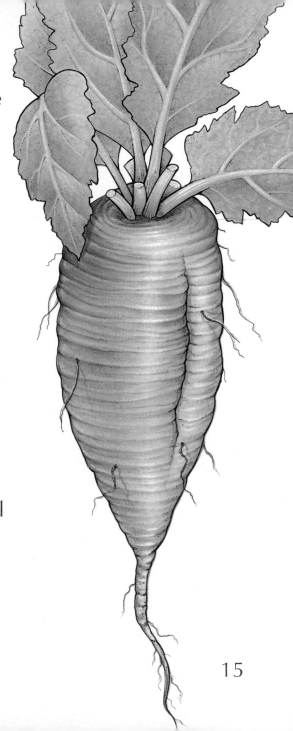

From farm to shop

Harvesting beets

The harvested sugar cane and beet are taken from the farm to a factory to be **refined**. Sugar beet is washed and sliced by machines, and the strips of beet are soaked in hot water to dissolve the sugar.

Sugar cane is cut up and the juice is either washed out with water, or squeezed out by huge

Cane arriving at factory

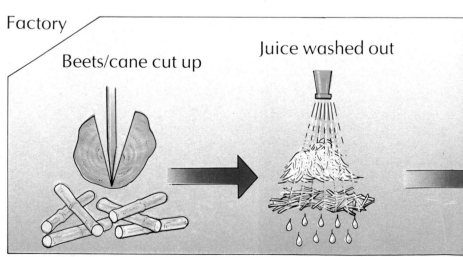

Factory

Beets/cane cut up

Juice washed out

rolling mills. It is then dissolved in tanks with water.

The sugar solution is purified and then boiled so that most of the water **evaporates** and a thick sugary syrup is left. The syrup is spun round in a huge drum which whirls round like a spin-drier. The sugar crystals which have formed stick to the sides of the drum and the remaining syrup, called molasses, is drained off. The brown crystals are further refined to turn them into white sugar.

This diagram shows how raw sugar cane and sugar beet are refined to make sugar crystals.

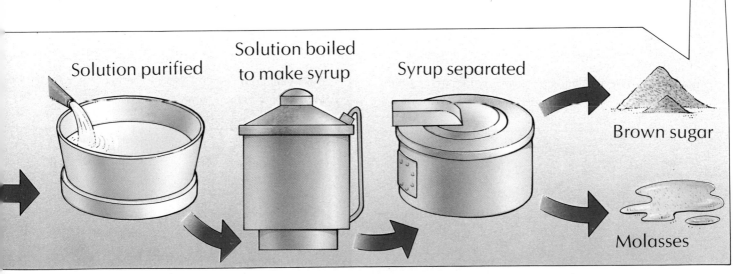

Solution purified

Solution boiled to make syrup

Syrup separated

Brown sugar

Molasses

Maple syrup is good to eat with pancakes. The sap from maple trees produces sugar in the form of syrup.

The sugar we eat

The thick, dark brown syrup that is left when the sugar has crystallized is called molasses. The sugar crystals are still covered in a fine layer of molasses at this stage, and this gives us dark brown sugar.

To make white sugar, all the syrup from the sugar crystals has to be removed. This is called refining sugar. **Granulated, caster** and **icing**

sugar are all types of refined sugar.

Nowadays, most types of soft and hard brown sugar, such as demerara, are made by refining the sugar first and then putting back some of the dark syrup. The syrup adds colour and flavour to the sugar.

Golden syrup is made from liquid sugar. Black treacle is made from a mixture of sugar and the molasses from sugar cane.

Above *A sugar cane juice maker in Pakistan. The cane is crushed and the juice is sold to thirsty passers-by.*

Right *Biscuits and icing are used to make this special cake as a treat for this German family.*

Opposite *This machine reduces the water content in the sugar solution during factory processing.*

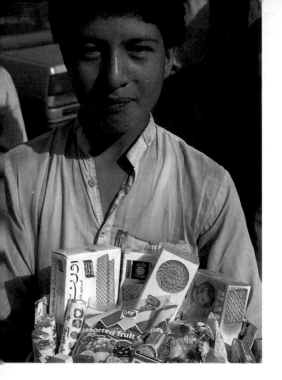

All kinds of uses

We can all think of sweet foods that contain sugar. But did you know that sugar is also added to some savoury foods? It is used in many canned and frozen vegetables, soups, cheeses, meats, ketchups and sauces. Bakers use sugar and yeast to make bread rise.

Sugar is used to preserve tobacco and leather,

Above *A boy sells a selection of sweet foods, made with sugar, at the roadside in Lahore, Pakistan.*

Right *Sugar cane for processing arriving at a factory in Mauritius.*

20

and even to make paints and some plastics. In Brazil, sugar cane is made into alcohol and can be used as a type of petrol to power cars.

The crushed sugar cane which is left after the sugar has been extracted can be used as fuel. It can also be mixed with other things to make paper, hardboard, animal feed and fertilizer. So sugar has many uses!

Crushing cane at a factory in Guadeloupe. When the juice has been taken out, the remaining cane will be used as fuel.

Sugar and your body

Sugar is a **carbohydrate**, a food which gives us energy. Our bodies can absorb the energy from sugar very quickly. That is why it is always included in **survival kits**.

However, too many sugary foods can be bad for us. If we eat too much sugar, our bodies turn it into fat and we become overweight. This can

This diagram shows how tooth decay is caused by sugar which has turned into acid in our mouths.

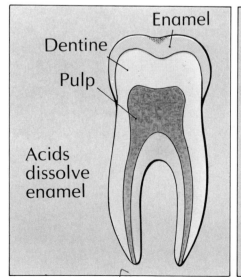

Enamel

Dentine

Pulp

Acids dissolve enamel

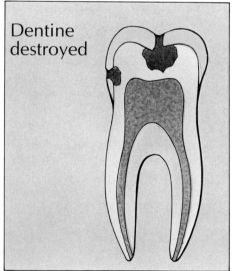

Dentine destroyed

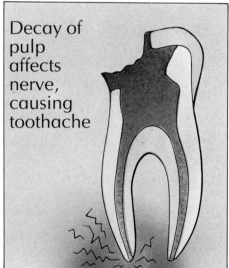

Decay of pulp affects nerve, causing toothache

Left *It is important to always clean our teeth after eating sugary foods such as this toffee apple.*

Below *Sweets such as these taste delicious, but we should try not to eat them too often.*

cause many serious illnesses. Sugar is also bad for teeth. It turns into acids in the mouth, which attack the protective **enamel** on our teeth and cause tooth decay.

This does not mean that we have to stop eating sugar altogether. But we should try not to eat sugary foods, such as sweets, cakes and biscuits, too often. And it is important that we always remember to brush our teeth regularly.

Sugar in the kitchen

A chef makes Easter bunnies out of marzipan, which is a paste made from sugar, ground almonds and egg whites.

We often add sugar to our food, and to drinks such as tea and coffee, because we like the sweet taste. It is also used when cooking many foods such as cakes, puddings and biscuits.

Sugar acts as a **preservative**, to help prevent food going mouldy. It is an important ingredient in jam, marmalade and bottled fruits.

Using sugar can be fun! You can make beautiful cake decorations out of icing sugar. The icing sugar is mixed with water and colourings into a smooth paste which can be made into many shapes. As it dries, the icing sugar hardens. You can see some ways of using sugar in the picture.

Try icing some biscuits with your own designs, using coloured icing and sugar decorations. You could make patterns or faces.

Honeycomb

You will need:

50g margarine
350g brown sugar
6 tablespoons honey
4 tablespoons water
2 teaspoons bicarbonate of soda
1 teaspoon vinegar

2. Bring the mixture to the boil and keep it bubbling, still stirring. Take a drop of the mixture and put it into a cupful of cold water. If the drop hardens, remove the saucepan from the heat.

3. Stir in the bicarbonate of soda and pour immediately into a small tin, lightly greased with margarine.

1. Put the margarine, sugar, honey, vinegar and water into a saucepan. Heat gently, stirring continuously until the sugar has completely dissolved.

4. Leave to cool. When cold, break into pieces.

Coconut ice

You will need:

8 tablespoons condensed milk
350g icing sugar
175g dessicated coconut
1 tablespoon cocoa powder
a few drops of pink food colouring

1. Lightly grease a square cake tin. Mix the milk and icing sugar together. Then stir in the coconut.

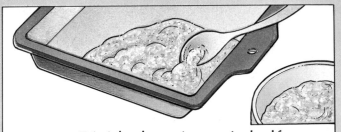

2. Divide the mixture in half. Add the colouring to one half and spread it into the cake tin.

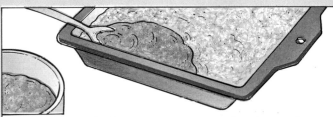

3. Sift the cocoa powder into the other half of the mixture and stir well. Spread this on top of the mixture already in the cake tin and leave to harden.

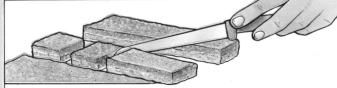

4. Cut the coconut ice into small squares.

Chocolate chip cookies

You will need:

150g self-raising flour
75g margarine
75g brown sugar
1 egg
½ teaspoon vanilla essence
¼ teaspoon salt
100g plain chocolate

2. Add the egg and vanilla essence and beat well.

1. Put the margarine and sugar into a bowl and mix them together.

3. Stir the flour and salt **gradually** into the mixture.

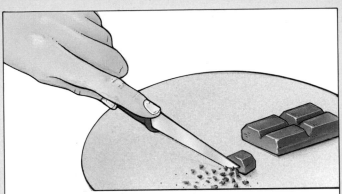

4. Cut the chocolate into tiny pieces and mix these into the biscuit dough.

5. Grease a baking tray with a bit of margarine. Take teaspoonfuls of the biscuit mixture and drop them on to the baking tray, leaving a little space around each one. Lightly press each heap of the mixture to flatten it slightly.

6. Bake in a oven at 160°C/ 325°F/ gas mark 3 for 10–15 minutes. Remember to wear oven gloves when using the oven, and be very careful.

Glossary

Absorb To soak or suck up.

Carbohydrates Foodstuffs which give us energy. Our bodies need energy all the time to walk, run and even to think.

Carbon dioxide A gas which is part of the air we breathe.

Caster sugar A finely ground white sugar, often used in foods such as cakes and biscuits.

Crusaders Christian warriors from Europe who fought battles to recapture the Holy Land from the Muslims during the Middle Ages.

Enamel The hard, smooth coating on teeth.

European Economic Community An economic association made up of Western European countries. Also known as the Common Market.

Evaporate When liquid is lost by changing into vapour.

Granulated sugar A coarsely ground white sugar.

Icing sugar Sugar which has been ground down into a very fine powder. It is used to make icing and other sweets.

Preservative A substance used to keep food fresh.

Refine To make something purer, or separate the coarser parts of a mixture out.

Substance The material or matter which makes up an object.

Survival kits Kits containing food and equipment to help people survive in difficult conditions in an emergency. They are carried by people such as mountaineers and fell walkers.

Temperate The areas of the world where the climate is warm in the summer, but cool or cold in the winter.

Tropical The areas of the world where the weather is very hot, usually with a lot of rainfall.

Books to read

A Spoonful of Sugar by D.A. Lucas (Wayland, 1982)
Focus on Sugar by Alan Blackwood (Wayland, 1985)
Sugar by V. Pitt (Franklin Watts, 1974)
Your Teeth by J. Iveson-Iveson (Wayland, 1982)

Index

Picture acknowledgements

The photographs in this book were provided by: British Sugar Bureau 7 (top), 14, 23 (bottom); David Cumming 6, 19 (top), 20; Mary Evans Picture Library 8, 9, 10; The Hutchison Library 11, 13, 21; Tate & Lyle 18; Zefa 7 (bottom), 19 (bottom), 20 (bottom), 23 (top), 24.